Maths

How to use this book with your child:

It is recommended that an adult spends time with a child while doing any kind of homework, to offer encouragement and guidance. Find a quiet place to work, preferably at a table, and encourage your child to hold his or her pen or pencil correctly.

Try to work at your child's pace and avoid spending too long on any one page or activity. Most of all, emphasise the fun element of what you are doing and enjoy this special and exciting time!

Don't forget to add a reward sticker to each page you complete!

Reward sticker!

Designed by Plum5
Illustrations by Sue King, Sharon Smart and Andy Geeson
Educational consultant Josh Levenson and Nina Filipek

Autumn
Publishing

Count to 100

What numbers are missing from this grid?
Fill in the missing numbers below.

1	2		4	5	6		8	9	10
11		13	14		16	17		19	
21	22	23		25		27	28		30
	32		34		36	37	38	39	40
41		43	44	45			48	49	
51	52		54		56	57	58		60
61	62	63		65	66	67		69	70
71	72	73	74		76		78	79	
81		83		85		87	88	89	90
	92		94	95	96	97		99	

Count up in 2s, 5s and 10s

Help the three frogs get to their lily pads by writing in the missing numbers in these sequences.

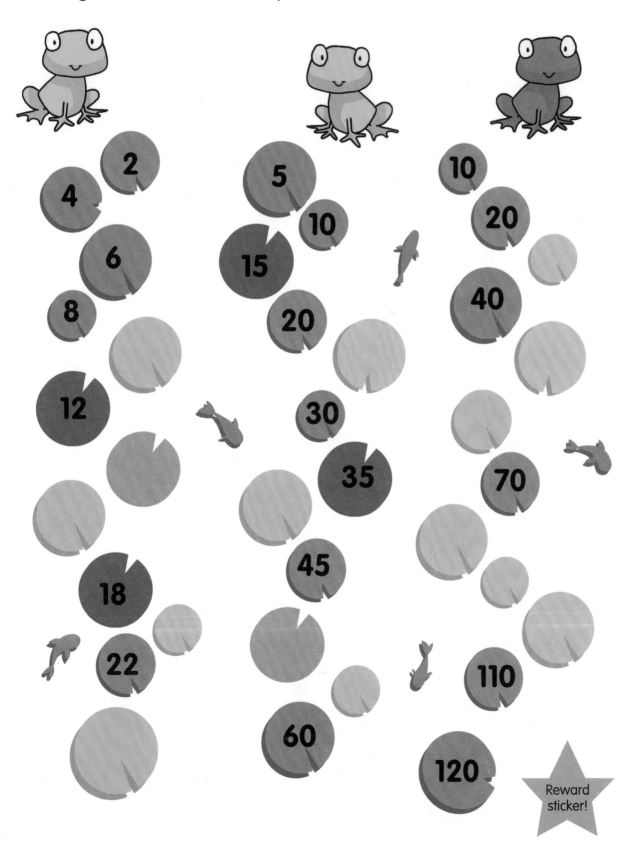

Reward sticker!

One more, one less

Practise adding and subtracting by 1 in the sums below.
Write the answers in the boxes.

E.g. $7 + 1 = \boxed{8}$ $2 - 1 = \boxed{1}$

$4 + 1 = \boxed{}$ $8 - 1 = \boxed{}$

$8 + 1 = \boxed{}$ $5 - 1 = \boxed{}$

$3 + 1 = \boxed{}$ $3 - 1 = \boxed{}$

$6 + 1 = \boxed{}$ $7 - 1 = \boxed{}$

Reward sticker!

Grouping

Put these bees into groups of 3.

How many groups are there?

How many bees are there altogether?

Put these sweets into groups of 4.

How many groups are there?

How many sweets are there altogether?

Reward sticker!

Adding up

Do the additions below, writing the answers in the boxes.

1 + 2 =

4 + 8 =

6 + 5 =

2 + 10 =

8 + 1 =

3 + 5 =

3 + 3 =

9 + 3 =

6 + 8 =

8 + 8 =

10 + 10 =

9 + 9 =

Reward sticker!

12 + 4 = ☐   8 + 3 = ☐

4 + 4 = ☐   10 + 11 = ☐

2 + 12 = ☐   11 + 12 = ☐

4 + 5 = ☐   10 + 6 = ☐

14 + 3 = ☐   8 + 7 = ☐

9 + 8 = ☐   11 + 8 = ☐

16 + 4 = ☐   16 + 5 = ☐

Taking away

Do the subtractions below, writing the answers in the boxes.

5 − 2 = ☐

7 − 2 = ☐

6 − 2 = ☐

13 − 12 = ☐

12 − 6 = ☐

20 − 11 = ☐

7 − 6 = ☐

18 − 9 = ☐

3 − 2 = ☐

16 − 14 = ☐

8 − 5 = ☐

4 − 2 = ☐

Reward sticker!

13 - 2 = ☐

8 - 5 = ☐

9 - 4 = ☐

12 - 8 = ☐

7 - 1 = ☐

8 - 2 = ☐

20 - 16 = ☐

15 - 13 = ☐

19 - 17 = ☐

17 - 12 = ☐

19 - 13 = ☐

15 - 8 = ☐

14 - 6 = ☐

13 - 5 = ☐

Reward sticker!

Fact families

A fact family is a group of three numbers, and the way that they relate to each other using addition and subtraction.

E.g. Here is a fact family for the numbers 3, 5 and 8.

- 3 + 5 = 8   • 5 + 3 = 8
- 8 − 5 = 3   8 − 3 = 5

Complete the following fact families.

- 2 + 5 = 7   • 5 + 2 = 7
- ___ − ___ = ___   ___ − ___ = ___

- 3 + 4 = 7   • ___ + ___ = ___
- ___ − ___ = ___   ___ − ___ = ___

- 1 + 8 = 9   • ___ + ___ = ___
- ___ − ___ = ___   ___ − ___ = ___

Reward sticker!

Here is a fact family for the numbers 13, 7 and 20.

- 13 + 7 = 20   • 7 + 13 = 20
- 20 − 7 = 13   • 20 − 13 = 7

Complete the following fact families.

- 14 + 6 = 20   • ___ + ___ = ___

- ___ − ___ = ___   • ___ − ___ = ___

- 12 + 8 = 20   • ___ + ___ = ___

- ___ 8− ___ = ___   • ___ − ___ = ___

- 17 + 3 = 20   • ___ + ___ = ___

- ___ − ___ = ___   • ___ − ___ = ___

Missing numbers

Fill in the missing numbers below to solve these out-of-this-world addition and subtraction sums.

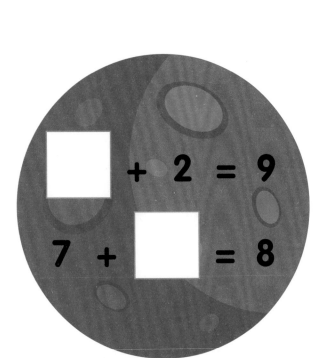

☐ + 2 = 9

7 + ☐ = 8

3 + ☐ = 7

9 − ☐ = 5

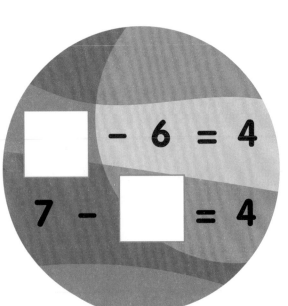

9 − ☐ = 4

☐ + 3 = 8

☐ − 6 = 4

7 − ☐ = 4

Reward sticker!

□ + 12 = 19

7 + □ = 15

3 + □ = 20

8 + □ = 17

□ − 6 = 11

16 − □ = 11

19 − □ = 14

□ + 3 = 18

Multiplying by 2

Complete this 2 times table grid.
Write the answers in the boxes below.

1 x 2 = ☐   7 x 2 = ☐

2 x 2 = ☐   8 x 2 = ☐

3 x 2 = ☐   9 x 2 = ☐

4 x 2 = ☐   10 x 2 = ☐

5 x 2 = ☐   11 x 2 = ☐

6 x 2 = ☐   12 x 2 = ☐

Reward sticker!

More multiplying by 2

Find the missing numbers for these 2 times table questions.
Write the answers in the boxes. We've done the first one for you.

$3 \times 2 = 6$ $\boxed{} \times 2 = 4$

$\boxed{} \times 2 = 16$ $\boxed{} \times 2 = 8$

$\boxed{} \times 2 = 20$ $\boxed{} \times 2 = 14$

$\boxed{} \times 2 = 18$ $\boxed{} \times 2 = 10$

Reward sticker!

Multiplying by 5

Complete this 5 times table grid.
Write the answers in the boxes below.

1 x 5 = ☐   7 x 5 = ☐

2 x 5 = ☐   8 x 5 = ☐

3 x 5 = ☐   9 x 5 = ☐

4 x 5 = ☐   10 x 5 = ☐

5 x 5 = ☐   11 x 5 = ☐

6 x 5 = ☐   12 x 5 = ☐

Reward sticker!

More multiplying by 5

Find the missing numbers for these 5 times table questions.
Write the answers in the boxes. We've done the first one for you.

| 3 | × 5 = 15 | | × 5 = 20 |

| | × 5 = 40 | | × 5 = 50 |

| | × 5 = 45 | | × 5 = 60 |

| | × 5 = 25 | | × 5 = 10 |

Reward sticker!

Multiplying by 10

Complete this 10 times table grid.
Write the answers in the boxes below.

1 x 10 =

7 x 10 =

2 x 10 =

8 x 10 =

3 x 10 =

9 x 10 =

4 x 10 =

10 x 10 =

5 x 10 =

11 x 10 =

6 x 10 =

12 x 10 =

Reward
sticker!

More multiplying by 10

Find the missing numbers for these 10 times table questions.
Write the answers in the boxes. We've done the first one for you.

$\boxed{3}$ x 10 = 30 $\boxed{}$ x 10 = 50

$\boxed{}$ x 10 = 80 $\boxed{}$ x 10 = 40

$\boxed{}$ x 10 = 90 $\boxed{}$ x 10 = 60

$\boxed{}$ x 10 = 100 $\boxed{}$ x 10 = 70

Reward sticker!

Double bubble

Double the numbers in each of the bubbles below.
Hint: **double 4** is the same as **4 + 4**.

Double 4

Double 9

Double 7

Double 6

Double 5

Double 8

Reward sticker!

2D shapes

A 2D (two-dimensional) shape is a shape that has length and width, but no depth (this means that it is flat).

Count all of the **squares** below. How many are there altogether? Write your answer in the box.

Count all of the **rectangles** below. How many are there altogether? Write your answer in the box.

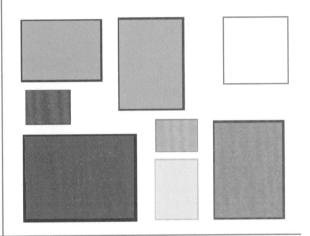

Count all of the **circles** below. How many are there altogether? Write your answer in the box.

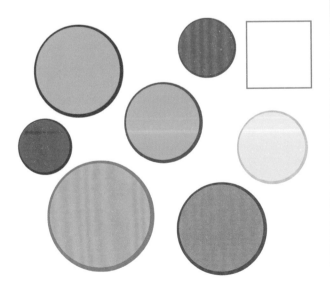

Count all of the **triangles** below. How many are there altogether? Write your answer in the box.

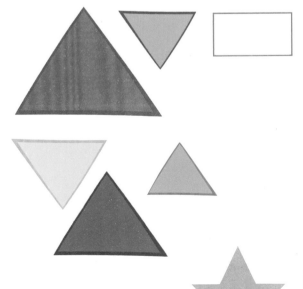

Reward sticker!

Halves

Shade in **half** of each of the shapes below.
The first shape has been done for you.

square

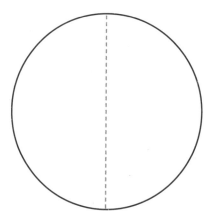

circle

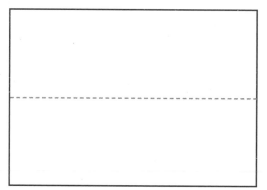

rectangle

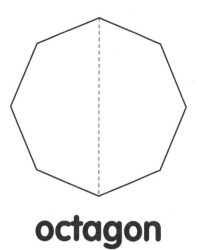

octagon

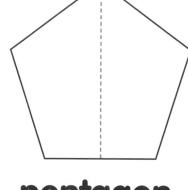

pentagon

Reward sticker!

Draw a ring around **half** of the objects for each of the below.
Then, read the questions and write your answers in the boxes.

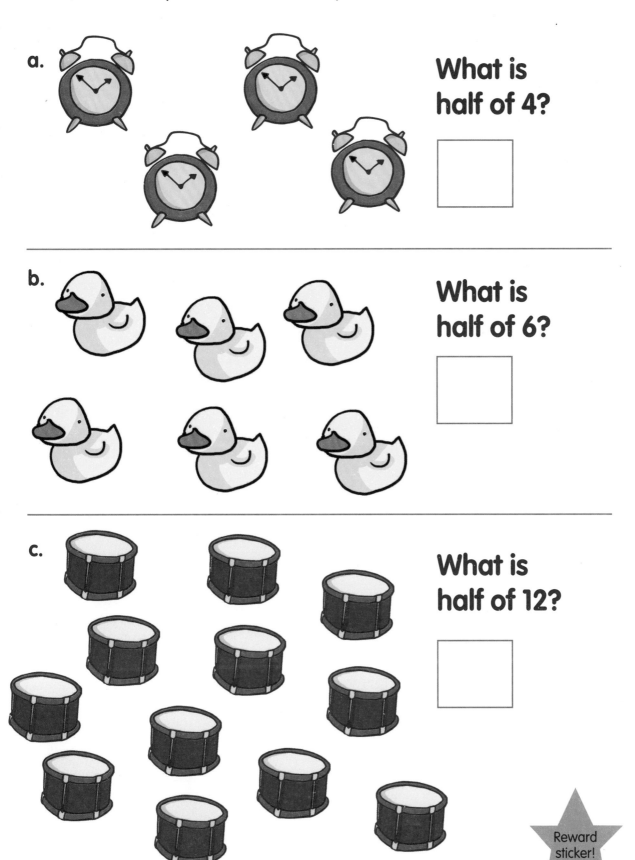

a.

What is half of 4?

b.

What is half of 6?

c.

What is half of 12?

Quarters

Shade in a **quarter** of each of the shapes below.
The first shape has been done for you.

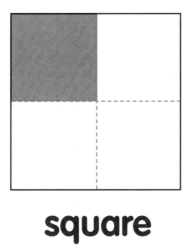

square

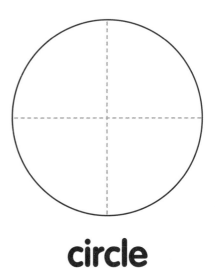

circle

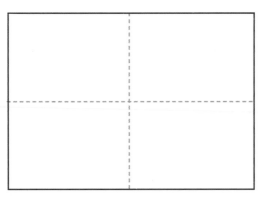

rectangle

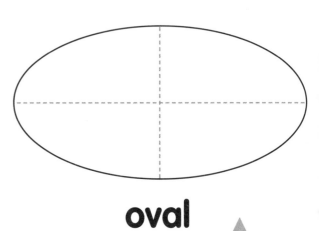

oval

Draw a ring around a **quarter** of the objects for each of the below.
Then, read the questions and write your answers in the boxes.

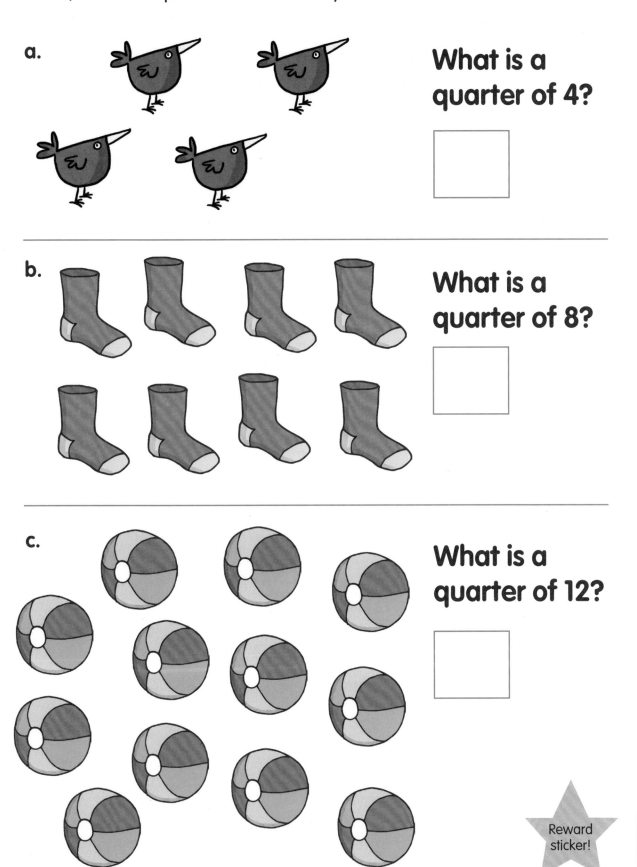

a.

What is a quarter of 4?

b.

What is a quarter of 8?

c.

What is a quarter of 12?

Reward sticker!

Coins

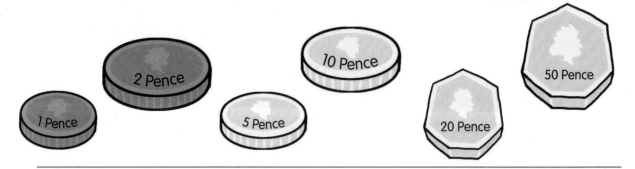

1 Pence 2 Pence 5 Pence 10 Pence 20 Pence 50 Pence

---

a. What two coins are these?

____ and ____

How much are they worth in total?

---

b. What two coins are these?

____ and ____

How much are they worth in total?

---

c. What two coins are these?

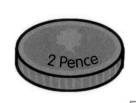 

____ and ____

How much are they worth in total?

3D shapes

A 3D (three-dimensional) shape is a shape that has length, width and depth. Take a look at the 3D shapes below.

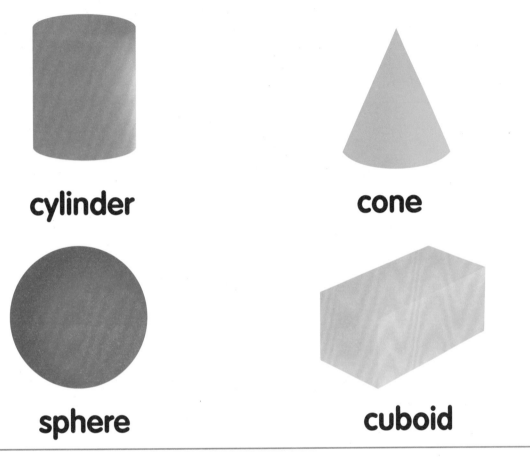

cylinder

cone

sphere

cuboid

This is a face

There are 6 faces on a cube.

How many faces does a cuboid have?

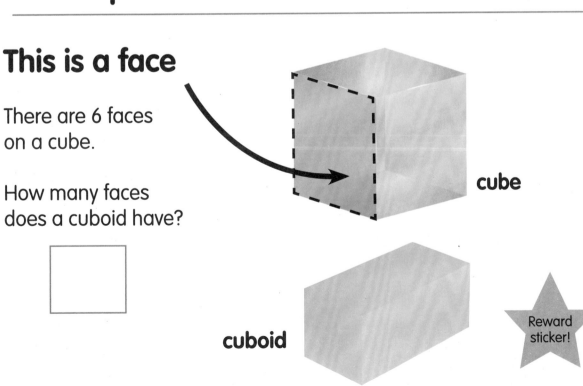

cube

cuboid

Reward sticker!

Colour by shapes

Follow the code to colour this picture.
Choose your own colours where there are no code symbols.

triangle

light blue

circle

light green

square

dark blue

star

dark green

Reward sticker!

Number patterns

Look carefully at these number cards.

| 1 | 2 | 3 | 4 | 5 | 6 | 7 | 8 | 9 | 10 |

Then, use the cards to complete the number patterns below.

a.  **2** 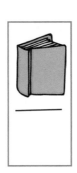 **4**    **10**

b. 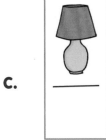  **3**   **7**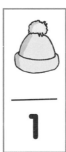

c.  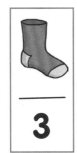  **3**  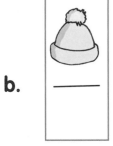 **1**

d.    **8** 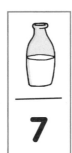 **7**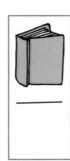

Reward sticker!

29

Mental maths

Answer the sums below in your head.
Write the answers in the boxes.

4 + 5 + 6 =

19 – 8 + 2 =

5 + 10 – 7 =

20 – 6 + 3 =

17 – 3 – 3 =

18 – 12 + 4 =

Reward sticker!

Answers:

Page 2: Count to 100

1	2	**3**	4	5	6	**7**	8	9	10
11	**12**	13	14	**15**	16	17	**18**	19	**20**
21	22	23	**24**	25	**26**	27	28	**29**	30
31	32	**33**	34	**35**	36	37	38	39	40
41	**42**	43	44	45	**46**	**47**	48	49	**50**
51	52	**53**	54	**55**	56	57	58	**59**	60
61	62	63	**64**	65	66	67	**68**	69	70
71	72	73	74	**75**	76	**77**	78	79	**80**
81	**82**	83	**84**	85	**86**	87	88	89	90
91	92	**93**	94	95	96	97	**98**	99	**100**

Page 3: Count up in 2s, 5s and 10s

2, 4, 6, 8, **10**, 12, **14**, **16**, 18, **20**, 22, **24**

5, 10, 15, 20, **25**, 30, 35, **40**, 45, **50**, **55**, 60

10, 20, **30**, 40, **50**, **60**, 70, **80**, **90**, **100**, 110, 120

Page 4: One more, one less

4 + 1 = **5**
8 + 1 = **9**
3 + 1 = **4**
6 + 1 = **7**
8 − 1 = **7**
5 − 1 = **4**
3 − 1 = **2**
7 − 1 = **6**

Page 5: Grouping

5 groups of bees, 15 bees altogether
3 groups of sweets, 12 sweets altogether

Pages 6-7: Adding up

1 + 2 = **3**	4 + 8 = **12**
6 + 5 = **11**	2 + 10 = **12**
8 + 1 = **9**	3 + 5 = **8**
3 + 3 = **6**	9 + 3 = **12**
6 + 8 = **14**	8 + 8 = **16**
10 + 10 = **20**	9 + 9 = **18**

12 + 4 = **16**	8 + 3 = **11**
4 + 4 = **8**	10 + 11 = **21**
2 + 12 = **14**	11 + 12 = **23**
4 + 5 = **9**	10 + 6 = **16**
14 + 3 = **17**	8 + 7 = **15**
9 + 8 = **17**	11 + 8 = **19**
16 + 4 = **20**	16 + 5 = **21**

Pages 8-9: Taking away

5 − 2 = **3**	7 − 2 = **5**
6 − 2 = **4**	13 − 12 = **1**
12 − 6 = **6**	20 − 11 = **9**
7 − 6 = **1**	18 − 9 = **9**
3 − 2 = **1**	16 − 14 = **2**
8 − 5 = **3**	4 − 2 = **2**

13 − 2 = **11**	8 − 5 = **3**
9 − 4 = **5**	12 − 8 = **4**
7 − 1 = **6**	8 − 2 = **6**
20 − 16 = **4**	15 − 13 = **2**
19 − 17 = **2**	17 − 12 = **5**
19 − 13 = **6**	15 − 8 = **7**
14 − 6 = **8**	13 − 5 = **8**

Pages 10-11: Fact families

7 − 5 = 2, 7 − 2 = 5
4 + 3 = 7, 7 − 4 = 3, 7 − 3 = 4
8 + 1 = 9, 9 − 8 = 1, 9 − 1 = 8
6 + 14 = 20, 20 − 6 = 14, 20 − 14 = 6
8 + 12 = 20, 20 − 8 = 12, 20 − 12 = 8
3 + 17 = 20, 20 − 3 = 17, 20 − 17 = 3

Pages 12-13: Missing numbers

7 + 2 = 9	7 + **1** = 8
3 + **4** = 7	9 − **4** = 5
9 − **5** = 4	**5** + 3 = 8
10 − 6 = 4	7 − **3** = 4
7 + 12 = 19	7 + **8** = 15
3 + **17** = 20	8 + **9** = 17
17 − 6 = 11	16 − **5** = 11
19 − **5** = 14	**15** + 3 = 18

Page 14: Multiplying by 2

1 x 2 = **2**	7 x 2 = **14**
2 x 2 = **4**	8 x 2 = **16**
3 x 2 = **6**	9 x 2 = **18**
4 x 2 = **8**	10 x 2 = **20**
5 x 2 = **10**	11 x 2 = **22**
6 x 2 = **12**	12 x 2 = **24**

Answers:

Page 15: More multiplying by 2

			2	x 2 =	4
8	x 2 =	16	4	x 2 =	8
10	x 2 =	20	7	x 2 =	14
9	x 2 =	18	5	x 2 =	10

Page 16: Multiplying by 5

1	x 5 =	**5**	7	x 5 =	**35**
2	x 5 =	**10**	8	x 5 =	**40**
3	x 5 =	**15**	9	x 5 =	**45**
4	x 5 =	**20**	10	x 5 =	**50**
5	x 5 =	**25**	11	x 5 =	**55**
6	x 5 =	**30**	12	x 5 =	**60**

Page 17: More multiplying by 5

			4	x 5 =	20
8	x 5 =	40	10	x 5 =	50
9	x 5 =	45	12	x 5 =	60
5	x 5 =	25	2	x 5 =	10

Page 18: Multiplying by 10

1	x 10 =	**10**	7	x 10 =	**70**
2	x 10 =	**20**	8	x 10 =	**80**
3	x 10 =	**30**	9	x 10 =	**90**
4	x 10 =	**40**	10	x 10 =	**100**
5	x 10 =	**50**	11	x 10 =	**110**
6	x 10 =	**60**	12	x 10 =	**120**

Page 19: More multiplying by 10

			5	x 10 =	50
8	x 10 =	80	4	x 10 =	40
9	x 10 =	90	6	x 10 =	60
10	x 10 =	100	7	x 10 =	70

Page 20: Double bubble

Double 4	=	**8**
Double 9	=	**18**
Double 7	=	**14**
Double 6	=	**12**
Double 5	=	**10**
Double 8	=	**16**

Page 21: 2D Shapes

6 squares	7 rectangles
7 circles	5 triangles

Pages 22-23: Halves

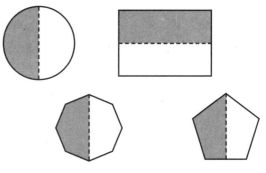

a. 2 **b.** 3 **c.** 6

Pages 24-25: Quarters

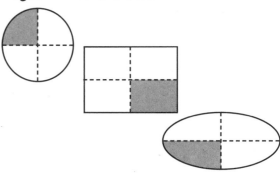

a. 1 **b.** 2 **c.** 3

Page 26: Coins

a. 1p + 10p = 11p
b. 20p + 5p = 25p
c. 2p + 50p = 52p

Page 27: 3D shapes

The cuboid has 6 faces.

Page 29: Number patterns

a. 2, 4, **6**, **8**, 10
b. **1**, 3, **5**, 7, **9**
c. **5**, **4**, 3, **2**, 1
d. **10**, **9**, 8, 7, **6**

Page 30: Mental maths

4 + 5 + 6 = **15**
19 − 8 + 2 = **13**
5 + 10 − 7 = **8**

20 − 6 + 3 = **17**
17 − 3 − 3 = **11**
18 − 12 + 4 = **10**